DREAMLAND

505 ACTIVITIES FOR KIDS

DREAMLAND PUBLICATIONS

J-128, Kirti Nagar, New Delhi-110 015, India
Tel : +91-11-2510 6050, 2543 5657
E-mail : dreamland@dreamlandpublications.com
Shop online at www.dreamlandpublications.com
Like us on www.facebook.com/DreamlandPublications

Look at the shapes and find their names from word search.

C	E	F	G	I	H	C	I	R	C	L	E
R	T	S	A	S	O	K	R	I	W	E	J
O	S	T	R	I	A	N	G	L	E	O	N
S	E	A	M	N	F	C	V	A	B	A	G
S	P	R	E	C	T	A	N	G	L	E	T
H	I	P	O	M	U	R	E	R	K	L	E
S	E	M	I	C	I	R	C	L	E	O	H
Q	P	I	D	M	A	O	T	C	R	A	E
U	S	K	U	I	M	W	V	S	R	E	A
A	Q	R	C	T	C	T	O	P	I	S	R
R	T	P	E	N	T	A	G	O	N	G	T
E	P	K	A	S	W	O	I	C	G	A	B

Draw a line to match the sense organs with their body parts.

Sense of Taste

Sense of Hearing

Sense of Sight

Sense of Smell

Choose the correct body part and write in the box.

NOSE, EYE, HAIR, EAR, HAND, CHEST, LEG, ANKLE

Find five differences between the two pictures.

Match the insects to their shadows.

Colour 2 foods from each meal which is healthy for our body.

From the given pictures cross the junk food and circle the healthy food.

Circle the animals which are small in size.

Write the shape names and complete the puzzle

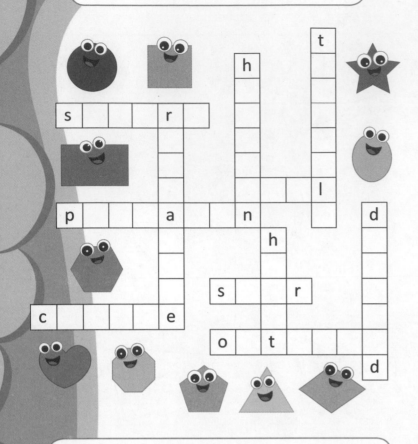

Find five differences between the two pictures.

Circle the heavy things and mark the light things.

Help Mom frog to find her baby.

What does not fit?

Select the right body part's name from the box and write against the arrows.

Eye   Antennae   Wings

Legs   Stinger

Find where animals live?

From the group of fishes find the same fish.

Match the expressions with their names.

Match the shapes with the same shape objects.

Happy

Sad

Angry

Surprise

Help the shapes to write their names in the given box.

Look at the small bird and copy its colour. Also write its name.

6

Colour the shapes according to given code, count them and write in the box.

Write the correct alphabet for each shape in the given circle.

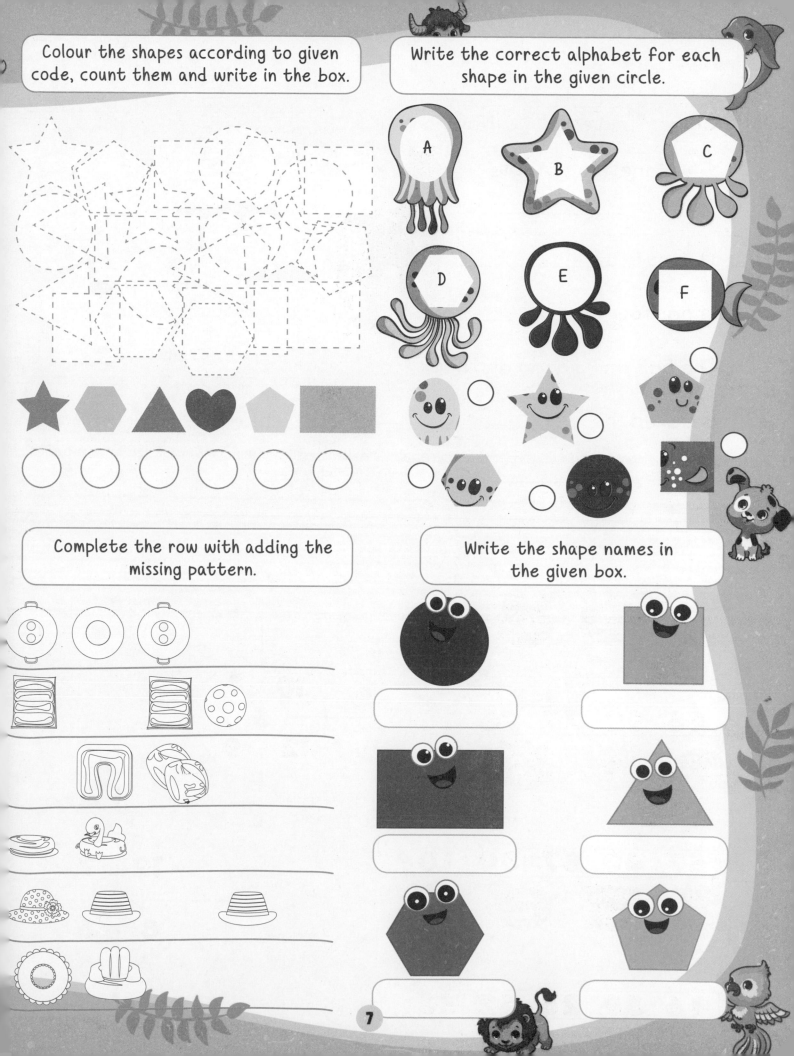

Complete the row with adding the missing pattern.

Write the shape names in the given box.

Choose the correct word and complete the sentence.

Horse   Legs   Hay

Mane   Stable

1. This is a _____

2. It lives in a _____

3. It has four _____

4. The hair on its head and neck

   is called the _____

5. It eats _____

Add and colour the number smaller than 20.

15+5   11+8

12+8   10+10

18+2   15+7

13+7   19+1

14+6   16+4

15+6   17+3

Write the numbers in order from least to greatest.

46 90 77 23 18

57 40 87 30 10

16 39 26 42 53

Add the centre number with each number and find the new number.

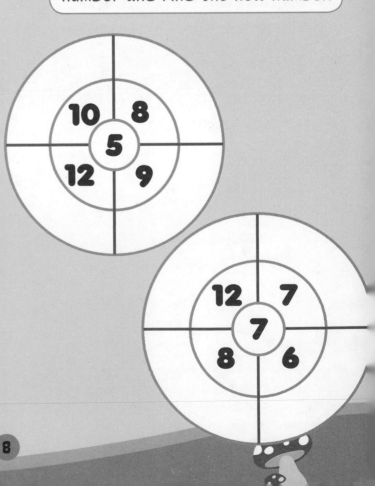

10   8
5
12   9

12   7
7
8   6

8

Draw a line to match the number name with its number.

Eight   ○   **48**

Second   ○   **4th**

Fourth   ○   **50**

Twenty   ○   **2nd**

Seventh   ○   **33**

Thirty three   ○   **20**

Fifty   ○   **7th**

Forty Eight   ○   **8**

Words go left, right, up, down, not diagonally, and can bend at a right angle. There are no unused letters in the grid, every letter is used only once.

S	S	H	A	S	H	C	R	A	B
T	I	S	R	K	E	L	L	N	A
G	N	E	A	H	O	D	O	C	E
R	A	Y	L	O	R	O	L	P	H
S	Q	U	S	B	S	H	W	H	I
T	D	I	T	O	E	S	L	A	N
U	R	T	E	C	F	I	E	L	R
J	E	L	R	T	O	P	U	A	E
E	S	E	A	B	E	D	S	R	E
L	L	Y	F	I	S	H	C	O	F

ANEMONE   COD   CORAL REEF   DOLPHIN
CRAB   FISH   FLYING FISH   HALIBUT
HERRING   JELLYFISH   LOBSTER   MORAY EEL
MUSSEL   OCEAN   OCTOPUS

Join the dots to complete the second half of the picture.

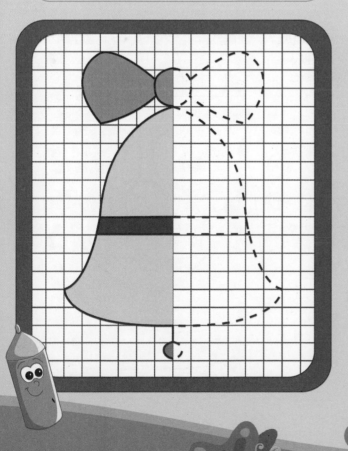

Match the flash card with its original picture.

Complete the cross word with the help of pictures.

Multiply the numbers inside the ball and circle the ones that match the number on the circle.

4X5 3X8 6X6	36 40
	2X5 5X8 6X6
3X5 5X5 4X6	25
	18 21
6X3 4X5 7X6	7X2 5X8 7X3

Write the correct alphabet for the missing part of the car.

Copy and colour.

10

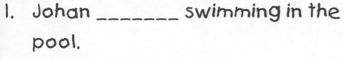

Fill in the blanks with is, am or are.

1. Johan _____ swimming in the pool.
2. The school bell _____ ringing .
3. I _____ Sally.
4. Ships _____ sailing in the sea.
5. I _____ not a cat.
6. Birds _____ flying in the sky.
7. We _____ happy.
8. Jam and Johany _____ friends.
9. These children _____ playing in the garden.
10. I _____ not an idot.

Complete the names by filling the correct vowels.

 S P _ D _ R

 B _ _

 L _ D Y B _ G

 B _ T T _ R F L Y

Draw a line to match the half face of each.

 ○   ○
 ○   ○
 ○   ○
 ○   ○
 ○   ○

Join the dots and colour it.

How many electric devices are here?

Mark the things which you will not carry while travelling.

Do the numbering of the things that you will put in the school bag.

Circle the Taj Mahal on the map.

Circle the picture postcards.

12

Write the alphabet for those things, you require during journey.

Cross the clothes, shoes and hat.

Find the Statue of Liberty.

Cross the travel guide book.

Write the correct number of puzzle piece in the given circle.

Match the shadow with its face.

 1

 2

 3

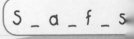

Circle the puzzle piece which is not its part.

Look at each picture and complete its name.

C_o_n_i_h   C__b   S_aH_r_e

J_ll_f_s_   T_r_t_e   S_a_f_s

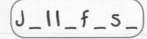
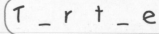

14

Help the young animals find their parents.

Match the animals' shadows with the animals.

Circle the living beings.

Help the Bee to find a way of her home.

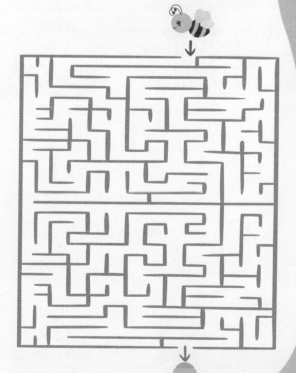

Match each picture with the correct word.

A Flower

B Seeds

C Cotyledon

D Adult plant

E Seedling

Look at each picture of a bird & fill in the missing vowels for each bird.

P_ng__n   P_rr_t   _wl

T_uc_n   D_ck   P__c_ck

D_v_   Sw_n   G__s_

Circle and write the beginning sound for each picture.

_ellyfish

L
J
I

_angaroo

G
X
K

Choose the word from the box and complete the sentence.

Play   Have   My   Like

I _____ a cap.

I _____ my friends.

I _____ with my ball

I love _____ dog.

16

Draw a line for each ball's name.

tennis

volleyball

soccer

bowling

basketball

beach

Circle the food items which you can taste with your tongue.

Do the calculation and according to answer colour the picture.

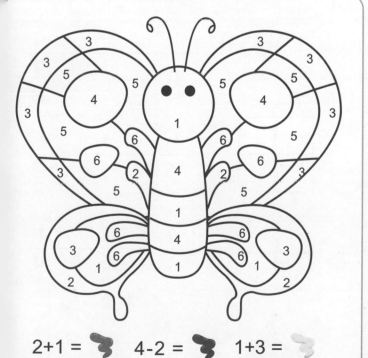

2+1 =

4-2 =

1+3 =

5-4 =

3+3 =

1+4 =

Read the words in each box and circle the words that rhyme.

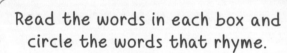

f a n

can	log	tan
van	jam	hit
man	bun	pan
rub	ran	nut
met	mug	ban

s i t

bug	wit	hit
tip	pit	fat
dog	fit	log
bit	hug	nit
met	lit	tub

Cross the fruits and circle the vegetables.

Use the picture to answer the question.

1. What fraction of the fruits are cherries ?

2. What fraction of the fruits are apples ?

3. What fraction of the fruits are green apples ?

4. What fraction of the fruits are strawberries ?

5. What fraction of the fruits are oranges ?

Draw the objects to complete the pattern.

Circle the correct fraction from the given choices.

$\dfrac{1}{2}$ $\qquad$ $\dfrac{2}{3}$ $\qquad$ $\dfrac{2}{4}$

$\dfrac{1}{3}$ $\qquad$ $\dfrac{3}{4}$ $\qquad$ $\dfrac{1}{2}$

$\dfrac{2}{4}$ $\qquad$ $\dfrac{3}{5}$ $\qquad$ $\dfrac{1}{4}$

$\dfrac{2}{3}$ $\qquad$ $\dfrac{1}{3}$ $\qquad$ $\dfrac{1}{2}$

18

Write the correct alphabet against its own shadow.

Circle the pictures that you can taste with your sense organ tongue.

Which item belongs to beach.

Match the fruit with its colour star.

19

Write the body parts names against the arrows.

Help the dog to get the bone.

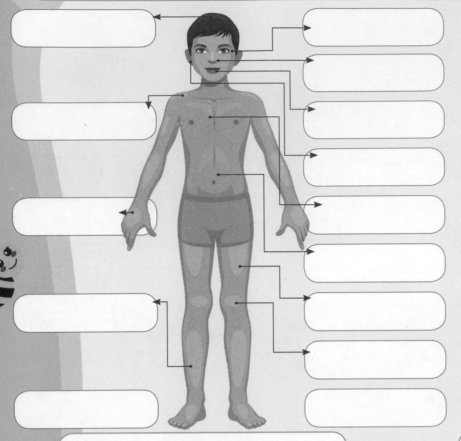

Label the plant's part with the given options.

Stem. Flower, Cotton, Seed Pod, Leaf

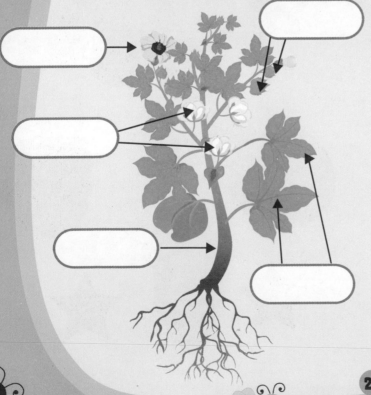

Find the following body parts name in word search.

Nose, Eye, Hair, Ear, Hand, Chest, Leg, Ankle

N	C	H	E	S	T	H	G
O	A	W	H	T	L	A	E
S	E	A	R	I	F	N	L
E	R	Y	H	G	F	D	E
E	O	N	A	E	Y	Z	L
Y	T	C	I	R	F	G	K
E	E	N	R	U	I	N	N
E	A	R	H	A	N	D	A

Look at the pictures and tell their state of matter (Solid, Gas, Liquid)

Draw a line to match the junk food with its name.

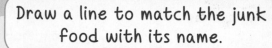

toffee

cookies

pudding

donut

cupcake

ice cream

lollipop

chocolate

popsicle

cake

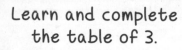

Complete the junk food name in cross word.

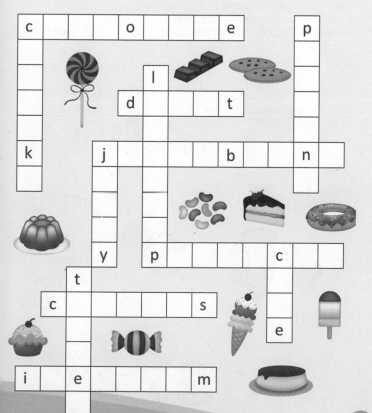

Learn and complete the table of 3.

3	X	1	=
3	X	2	=
3	X	3	=
3	X	4	=
3	X	5	=
3	X	6	=
3	X	7	=
3	X	8	=
3	X	9	=
3	X	10	=
3	X	11	=
3	X	12	=

Draw a line to match the animals with their home.

Draw a line to match the animals with their patterns.

Find the name of the picture and colour it.

J	E	L	L
C	R	A	B
A	B	T	Y
J	K	I	R
K	L	R	G

Circle all the reptiles in the given pictures.

What of the 2-10 are the missing fragments of the picture.

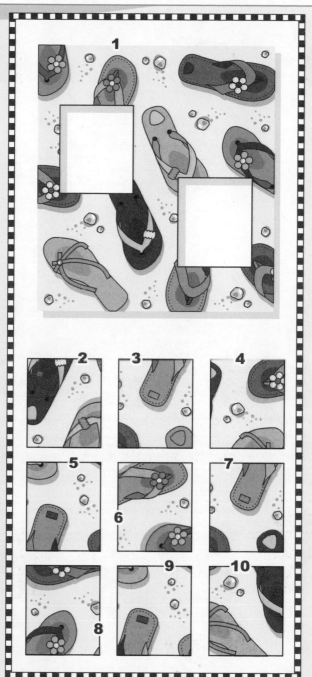

Match the words and write the compound word.

Cob   ○   Ball   _____

Eye   ○   Light   _____

Moon   ○   Crow   _____

Scare   ○   Craft   _____

Witch   ○   Web   _____

Let's do 2 digit number addition.

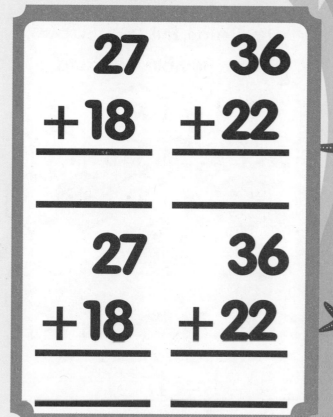

$$27 \quad 36$$
$$+18 \quad +22$$

$$27 \quad 36$$
$$+18 \quad +22$$

Use each hint to write a word that is only one letter different than the word above it.

COAL   SAIL   TALL

TAIL   SOIL   COIL

1. The opposite of short _____

2. The hind part of an animal _____

3. Put to sea _____

4. Dirt _____

5. Spiral _____

6. Dark mineral used for fuel _____

Fit the words into the honeycomb. Each word start in a bright yellow cell and wind clockwise around an arrange cell.

Delete, Detail, Rubbed, Elbows, Plates , Bumble, Worded

Look at the vegetables and find their names in word search.

C	A	R	R	O	T	R	W	P	E
P	E	P	P	W	Q	X	R	U	G
C	T	O	M	A	T	O	A	M	G
O	V	E	G	C	V	G	D	P	P
R	R	T	E	T	O	M	I	K	L
N	P	E	P	P	E	R	S	I	A
C	A	P	B	A	G	E	H	N	N
W	P	O	T	A	T	O	E	S	T
C	U	C	U	M	B	E	R	A	Q
W	R	G	D	W	S	A	A	F	I
P	O	T	A	F	P	G	T	S	F

Match each picture with its name.

Fruit   Vegetable   Dairy

Grains   Protein

Match the animals with their shadows.

How is it done? Which 2 pieces were used to produce the pattern 5?

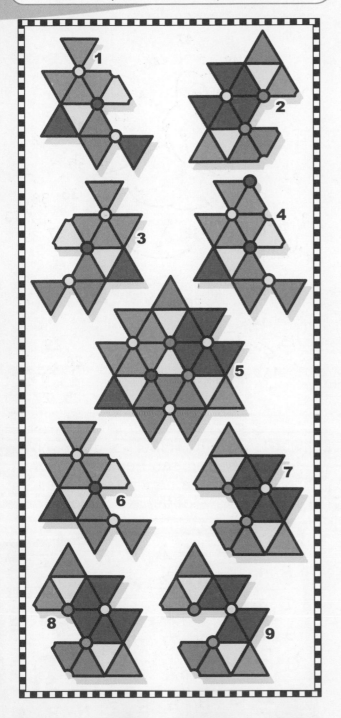

Help the animals to get their babies. Match through the lines.

Circle the things which we use while taking bath.

Natural Soap

Write the correct alphabet against the animals' babies.

(A) Cub	(F) Cub
(B) Calf	(G) Calf
(C) Baby	(H) Joe
(D) Calf	(I) Cub
(E) Foal	(J) Pup

Solve the rope and write the end alphabet in the box and you will find its name.

E   I   R   D   N   F   S

Join the dots and colour the picture.

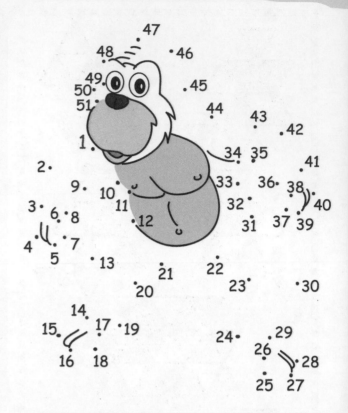

Look at the pictures and unscramble the letters to name the Dino.

rannoustysaur exr

Words go left, right, up, down, not diagonally, and can bend at a right angle. There are no unused letters in the grid, every letter is used only once.

S	A	L	M	A	N	E	M	E	T
S	M	O	O	P	N	K	O	N	U
T	A	R	N	L	A	T	O	N	B
S	R	A	Y	U	R	M	L	E	I
C	F	I	E	E	C	U	S	S	L
U	B	S	H	L	H	I	N	H	A
C	A	D	I	V	O	T	E	R	D
O	D	G	N	I	Y	S	G	S	E
F	I	N	H	S	E	H	N	E	E
L	Y	G	F	I	R	R	I	A	W

OYSTER PLANKTON SALMON SCUBA DIVING
SEABED SEAHORSE SEAWEED SHARK SHELL
SQUID STARFISH STINGRAY TURTLE WHALE

Help the little hungry caterpillar to get to the yummy green breakfast.

Find the animals name which you see in the farm.

C	M	E	R	C	U	R
H	G	O	A	T	A	K
I	S	R	C	O	W	E
C	H	T	U	R	N	H
K	E	H	P	O	E	O
E	E	O	W	O	P	R
N	P	V	A	S	T	S
D	O	G	P	T	U	E
D	U	C	K	E	N	V
J	U	P	I	R	E	R

Goat, Chicken, Cow, Sheep, Rooster, Dog, Duck, Horse

Circle and write the beginning sound for each picture.

1
2
3
4
5
6
7
8

_ion

T L J

_adybug

L J T

Fill the missing number to complete the equations.

$10 + \_\_\_ + 8 = 33$

$18 + \_\_\_ + 5 = 39$

$21 + \_\_\_ + 6 = 47$

$33 + \_\_\_ + 3 = 65$

$25 + \_\_\_ + 9 = 62$

Fill in the missing letters.

This is a __ow.

This is a s____P.

This is a r___s___r.

This is a h__rs__.

This is a ____o__e.

This is a g_____.

Find the odd one out.

Rearrange the letters to form the months of the years.

uaryjan _____

ruaryfeb _____

rchma _____

rilap _____

aym _____

neju _____

lyju _____

ustaug _____

embersept _____

berocto _____

embernov _____

berdecem _____

Help the Monster to come out from the space shuttle.

28

Match the opposite words.

HOT	HEAVY
NEW	COLD
LIGHT	OLD
NIGHT	TALL
SHORT	SMALL
NEAR	OUTSIDE
BIG	DAY
INSIDE	FAR

Look at the alien and copy the colour.

Fill in each blank with the correct word from the box.

Monday, Tuesday, Wednesday, Thursday, Friday, Saturday, Sunday

1. _____ is between Tuesday and Thursday.
2. The day after Wednesday is _____.
3. _____ comes after Thursday.
4. The weekends fall on _____ and _____.
5. The First working day of the week is _____.
6. The day that comes before Wednesday is _____.
7. Which is your favourite day of the week? _____.

Unscramble the word and write the name in given box.

TASRUN _____

Help the Shuttle to reach on planet.

Find the five differences between the two pictures.

Write the name of vegetables and fruits.

Unscramble the letters and name me.

RATPIES _____

Do the simple additions and write the sum in the given box.

15 + 12 =

26 + 23 =

30 + 28 =

Colour it and write its name.

G

31

Circle the musical instruments.

Write the missing letter for each word (a.e)

 **_nt**

 **_llig_tor**

 **V_n**

 **_gg**

Circle the word that is not rhyming word.

| BLUE | SHOE | JACKET |

| BEANS | BELT | JEANS |

| MESS | DRESS | SKIRT |

Help the Monster to reach planet.

Help pluto to reach its food by following the directions.

Match the sentences with the functions of sense organs.

I CAN SMELL.   **I CAN HEAR.**

I CAN TASTE.   **I CAN FEEL.**

Draw a Red line from the word Hard to the things that feel hard a Blue line from the word Soft to the things that feel soft.

Match the fruit with its characteristic.

Juicy Fruit

Pulpy Fruit

HARD

SOFT

Help the witch to reach the castle.

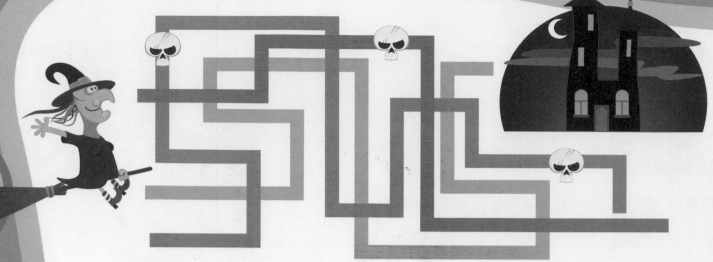

Look at the pictures and join them with their names.

Bat

Hat

Skull

Ghost

Pumpkin

Spiderweb

Find two identical pictures.

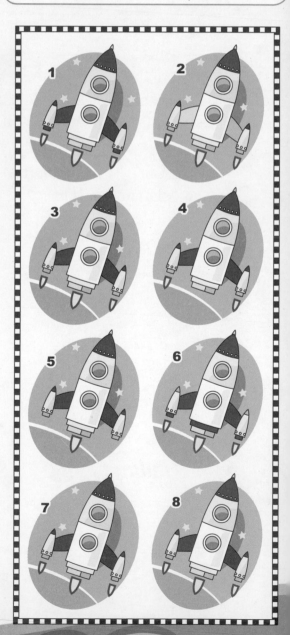

1   2

3   4

5   6

7   8

Find the correct shadow.

Find the five differences between two pictures.

Match the parts.

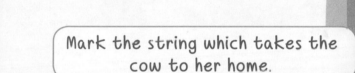

Mark the string which takes the cow to her home.

Write the numbers 5 less than and 5 more than the number shown.

5 less   5 more

◯ ↔ **25** ↔ ◯

◯ ↔ **48** ↔ ◯

◯ ↔ **36** ↔ ◯

2 less than 4

2 less than 8

2 less than 3

An antonym is a word opposite in meaning to another.

1. FIX ⚪ LIGHT
2. DUMB ⚪ RIGHT
3. TALL ⚪ POOR
4. SLEEPY ⚪ BREAK
5. FAST ⚪ SMART
6. HAPPY ⚪ SLOW
7. BIG ⚪ AWAKE
8. RICH ⚪ SHORT
9. LEFT ⚪ SAD
10. DARK ⚪ SMALL

Solve the sum then look at the colour code to colour the picture.

1 =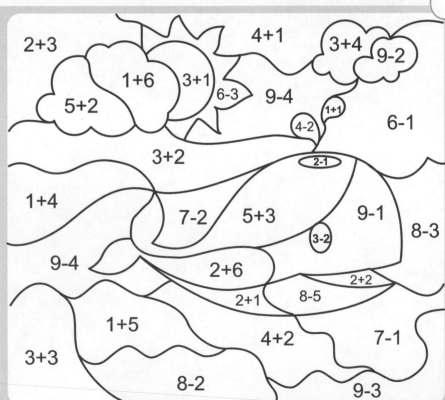
2 =
3 =
4 =
5 =
6 =
7 =
8 =

What will be the sum of these numbers?

05+
10+
15+
20+
25+
___

___

36

How many pieces of watermelon has Johan got?

How many pieces of watermelon Jimmy has got?

How many pieces of watermelon has Johan got than Jimmy?

Draw more pieces of watermelon for Jimmy so that he has 10 pieces.

Find the hidden pirates.

Do the addition correctly it will take you to the treasure.

2 +

How many Yellow fishes are there?

Find the single turtle.

Find the red crabs.

Find and name the big ocean animal.

Find and count the fish skull .

Find the gift box and write its name.

$7 + 8 + 9 + 11 + 13 + 15 + 16 =$

Circle the beginning sound for each picture and write it.

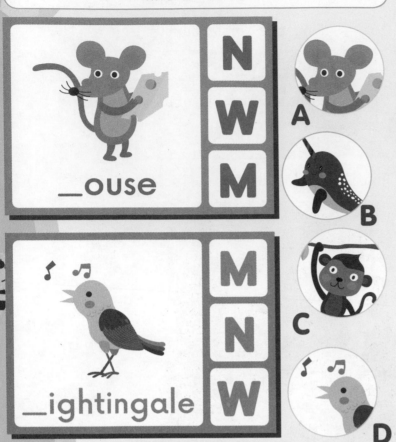

N W M

_ouse

M N W

_ightingale

A
B
C
D

Read each row of words and circle the two words that are antonyms.

FAST   QUICK   SLOW   ANGRY

TALL   FAT   QUICK   SHORT

FAST   UPSET   BIG   HAPPY

GO   SLOW   COME   SHORT

NO   NOD   YES   HOT

FUN   CRY   OLD   NEW

QUICK   SAD   RIGHT   LEFT

Draw a line from start to end, connecting the rhyming words.

Start

pan	yam	ham	bag	rag
can	fan	ham	tag	yam
yam	man	pan	jam	bag
jam	ham	can	fan	man
bag	rag	ham	can	pan
tag	jam	man	fan	yam

End

Find the right way to reach the castle.

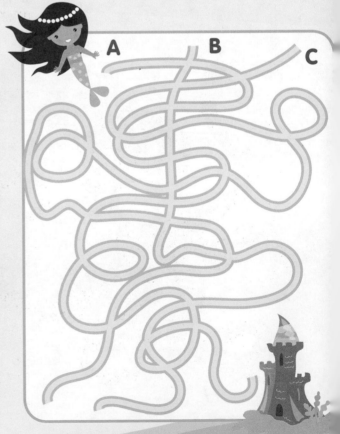

A
B
C

Fill in the blanks using same pictures as the above set has. When you finish, there should be only one of each picture in a row & in a column.

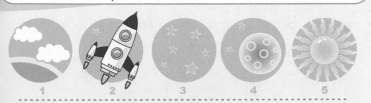

Draw a line to find who is the mom of this chick.

Can you find the greatest and the smallest numbers in each row?

(A) 3014, 2938, 7563, 431, 12191

(B) 2819, 8762, 10229, 1817

(C) 9871, 2876, 7659, 34621

Arrange the following numbers in ascending order.

(A) 2887, 2807, 8287, 7582

(B) 7662, 2679, 79291, 8372

(C) 58359, 23472, 5432, 90392

What is the expanded form of the number?

4 8 7 6 3

Write the missing letter for each word. (a,e)

Z_br_

J_m

C_ndl_

Y_rn

Who am I? Write my name in the given box.

Write the number against the correct weather.

1. SPRING   2. SUMMER   3. AUTUMN   4. WINTER

Arctic animals word search.

O	T	H	A	F	O	P	D	I	P	S	K
E	A	R	T	R	E	I	N	D	E	E	R
V	O	T	E	E	A	T	S	K	U	A	K
N	A	R	W	H	A	L	H	F	I	L	D
N	B	A	A	G	E	S	Z	L	R	N	C
E	P	O	L	A	R	B	E	A	R	P	B
R	E	I	R	H	E	O	K	B	E	A	I
P	N	K	U	O	M	O	O	S	E	R	S
H	G	I	S	G	W	H	A	F	A	E	O
F	U	W	L	R	U	B	E	A	G	E	N
K	I	L	L	E	R	W	H	A	L	E	T
X	N	Y	N	G	Y	M	O	N	E	K	Y

What's the temperature!

MON	TUE	WED	THU	FRI	SAT	SUN
21°	26°	24°	20°	22°	18°	15°

Arrange the following numbers in descending order.

A) 85885, 56868, 5568, 95673

B) 48329, 23892, 234849, 36480

C) 32823, 32283, 22823, 32283

In Indian System of Numeration, the number **286549872** is written, using commas, as_____

Match the name with its picture.

SOLDIER   LAWN TENNIS PLAYER   GOLF PLAYER   DOCTOR   CHEF

Write the correct alphabet against bird's name.

SWAN

PEACOCK

TOUCAN

OWL

EAGLE

PARROT

Look at the pictures and fill in the missing vowels for each space word.

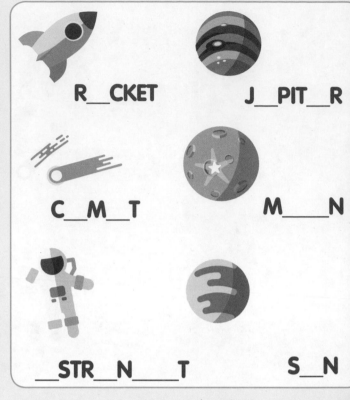

R__CKET

J__PIT__R

C__M__T

M___N

__STR__N___T

S__N

Count the vegetables and write the number against its picture.

Find the correct shadow.

A

B

C

D

44

Write the alphabet for each shape to complete the picture.

Colour me and write my name in the box.

Match the footprints with its name.

Tiger

Leopard

Lizard

Hippo

Koala

Join the dots and colour the picture.

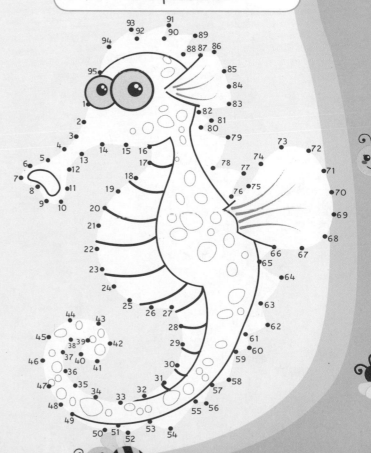

Rearrange the letters to form the name of a colour then colour the balloons.

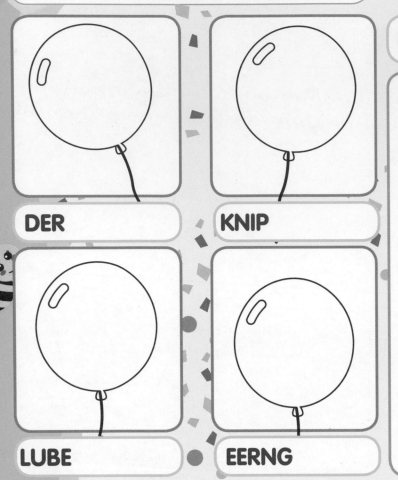

DER

KNIP

LUBE

EERNG

Who is he?

Baker   Doctor   Postman   Farmer

He delivers letters.

He is a _____.

We go to her when we are ill.

She is a _____.

He grows fruits and vegetables.

He is a _____.

He bakes bread.

He is a _____.

Match the Tangram shadows.

Match the missing part of each animal.

A
B
C
D
E

Match each person with the correct place.

Look at each picture of animals and fill in the missing vowels for each bird.

T__rk__y

G__ __t

Sh__ __p

C__w

Mary wants to go out. Fill in the letters to find out where she wants to go.

Code

1=a   7=n
2=e   8=o
3=g   9=p
4=h   10=r
5=i   11=t
6=k   12=w

5 12 1 7 11 11 8 3 8
_____

11 8 11 4 2 9 1 10 6
_____

Fill in the letters to find out where Tom is going.

Code 1=a 2=b 3=c 4=e
5=h 6=o 7=t

7 5 4   2 4 1 3 5
_____

Draw a line from picture on left to the matching picture on right.

Match the pictures to their shadows.

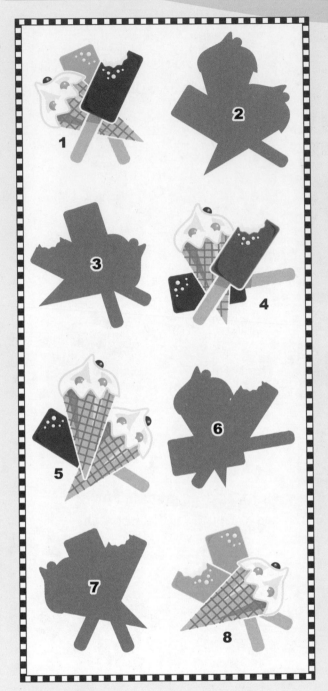

Learn and complete the table of 5.

5 X 1 =
5 X 2 =
5 X 3 =
5 X 4 =
5 X 5 =
5 X 6 =
5 X 7 =
5 X 8 =
5 X 9 =
5 X 10 =
5 X 11 =
5 X 12 =

Rearrange the letters and write my name.

NAUTROTAS

48

Whom do these stripes belong to?

The Panda

The Zebra

The Giraffe   **The Cheetah**

Solve the sums on the dog's bone and match with the answers.

1 + 2

3 + 1

7 − 6

6 − 4   2 + 3

① ② ③ ④ ⑤

Circle the things you can find in your school.

SCALE

PENCIL   **ERASER**

BAG

BALL

BLENDER

HAT

GLOBE

CRAYONS

APPLE   **BOOK**   **PAN**

Match the things with its name.

Runner bean

Green bean

Okra

Peanut

Ricebean

Indian pea

49

Put a right mark in the correct boxes.

Circle the things that are noisy.

	THINGS TO EAT	THINGS TO DRINK	THINGS I LIKE	THINGS I DON'T LIKE
EGG				
CHICKEN				
WATER				
RICE				
BREAD				
MILK				
FISH				
ICE-CREAM				
HAMBURGER				
APPLE				

Look at the pictures and write their names against their number.

Match the correct shadow of mummy.

Write correct alphabet against its name.

- WALLET
- PANTS
- T-SHIRT
- SHIRT
- BLAZER
- SHOE

From A to E which alphabet will fit to complete the picture. Write in the circle.

Cross the animals that do not belong to the farm.

Find the Snail.

How many Chicks are there? Count and write in the circle.

Name the animal that is hiding behind the Turkey.

How many sheep are there?

How many ducklings are there in the pond?

How many birds are there in the sky?

Circle the animal who gives milk.

Can you find the horse?

Count the number of the apples on the tree.

Match the temperature with their thermometer.

29°C

-9°C

26°C

-6°C

40°C

5°C

2°C

Find the five differences between two pictures.

Can you find out two animals that do not belong to the group?

Help the Butterfly to find the shortest way to reach the flower.

A
B
C

Find the names of Desert animals in cross word.

Match the correct shadow.

A

B

C

Unscramble the names of water animals.

ALEWH _____

ABCR _____

OISETORT _____

FIJESHLLY _____

Match each Guitar with its shadow.

Rearrange the words to form a sentence. Write it in the blank.

1. six i am year old

   _____

2. this bag heavy is

   _____

3. today monday is

   _____

4. tall boy is jack a

   _____

5. there are in a rainbow seven colours

   _____

Look at the pictures and complete their names.

P__M__K__N

W__T__H

W__T__H

H____T

__A__I__ W__N__

B____

S____D____ __E__

Match the butterflies with their second half.

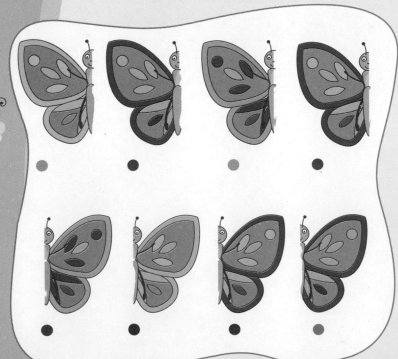

Match the monsters with their other half.

Who is hiding in the boxes?

Write the correct Alphabet in given space.

Help Alina to find her dog.

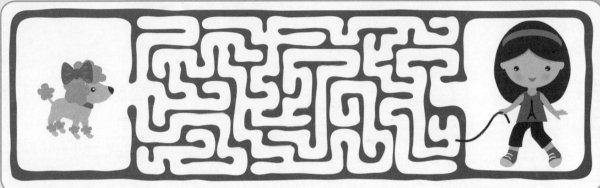

Circle the correct shadow.

Write down the names of 5 vegetables.

1. _____

2. _____

3. _____

4. _____

5. _____

Look at each picture and tick the right answer.

Fruits	Colour of the fruits
Cherry	Green
Orange	Red
Lemon	Pink
Plum	Orange
Grapes	Purple
Durian	Yellow

Up / Down   **Young / Old**

Dirty / Clean   **Tired / Fresh**

Mathematical Puzzle

Colour and name the animal.

Fill in the blanks with a or an.

1. That is _____ dog.

2. The nurse gave him _____pill

3. Do you have _____ umbrella?

4. We are going to watch _____ movie.

5. Mother is peeling _____ orange.

Unscramble the letters and find the name of animal.

INNGPEU

1. Lilly (read, reads) a book.

2. Alex (eat, eats) a cake after dinner.

3. The hungry babies (cry, cries) loudly.

4. Tracy (wears, wear) her blue dress to the party.

5. The men (drop, drops) some eggs.

6. The girls (sings, sing) sweetly.

7. Johan (go, goes) to the market.

8. Jimmy (play, plays) the cricket.

Find the animal category.

Farm Animals

Jungle Animals

Reptiles

Birds

Match the currency with their sign.

$ •   Yen

€ •   Dollar

£ •   Pound

¥ •   Euro

Help the man to reach his van.

Count the monsters and write the number against them.

Follow the letter U to reach the umbrella.

Umbrella

Z	Q	U	U	U	D
O	N	U	Y	U	U
U	F	L	U	U	P	H	U
U	U	H	U	A	V	U	U
I	U	F	U	C	R	U	Z
K	U	S	U	X	
M	U	U	U	E	
J	T	B	G	W	

Uu

U

Look at the picture and find the name.

Scuba Diver   Sky Diver   Paragliding

Find five differences in the pictures.

Guess which animals' skins are these. Name them.

Write the names of colours in the box given below.

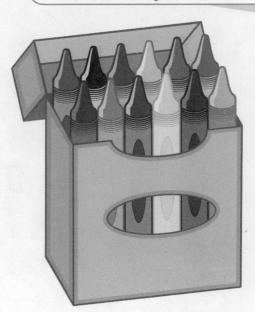

Match the shadows.

Connect the dots and colour the picture.

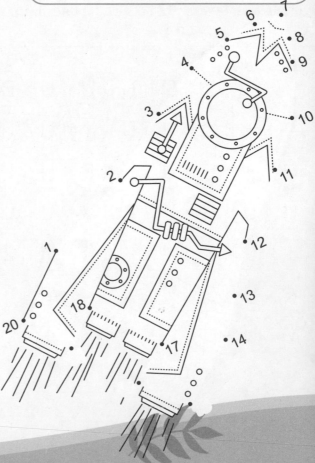

Match the names with their pictures.

 Santa

 **Rain deer**

 **Stocking**

 **Elves**

Snowman

 Christmas tree

Colour the picture according to colour code.

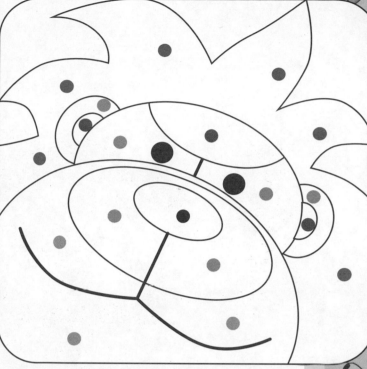

Solve the table of 8

$$8 \times 1 =$$
$$8 \times 2 =$$
$$8 \times 3 =$$
$$8 \times 4 =$$
$$8 \times 5 =$$
$$8 \times 6 =$$
$$8 \times 7 =$$
$$8 \times 8 =$$
$$8 \times 9 =$$
$$8 \times 10 =$$
$$8 \times 11 =$$
$$8 \times 12 =$$

Circle the odd one out in each row.

How many cats are there?

How many cats are behind the birds house?

Circle the cat who is watching the cloud.

How many cats are hiding themselves in the grass?

How many cats are there on the wall?

Circle the cat who wants yellow flower.

Circle the cat on the log.

Mark the cats who are playing with the things.

Circle the cat hanging on the tree.

Mark the cat flying with red balloon.

Help the pirate to get the treasure.

Tick the right name of this picture.

IRON-MAN   SPIDER MAN

Find 10 differences in the given pictures.

Draw a line to match the weather with its name.

  Snow

Rainy

  Cloudy

Sunny

  Thunder

Storm

  Clear

Night

  Rain with Thunder

66

Match the pictures with their sun signs.

Aries

Scorpio

Libra

Virgo

Help the cow to get home.

Can you find the 5 differences between two pictures?

Search the planets name in the word search.

```
E M E R C U R Y H T V
P D A F T A K E A W E
N E R G O T E L I H N
S A T U R N E R A U U
E L H P Y E T M A R S
A S E D O P N G E A T
P E V A H T C I N N P
A T E P L U T O N J C
E C I N E N V A H S E
J U P I T E R D A T Y
```

SATURN   EARTH   VENUS
MERCURY JUPITER NEPTUNE

Help dino moms to find their eggs.

Write A for tall animals, B for the taller and C for the tallest animals.

Put a 'C' beside the countable noun & a 'U' for the uncountable noun.

Hair ( )

Spider ( )

Rainbow ( )

Coffee ( )

Flower ( )

Balloon ( )

Match the words on the left to its opposite on the right.

SWEET ● ● FEW

BIG ● ● SOUR

MANY ● ● SLOW

FRESH ● ● SMALL

FAST ● ● AWAKE

SLEEPING ● ● STALE

Fill in each blank with the correct word from the box.

1. This first month of the year is

   _____

2. Christmas fall in the month of

   _____

3. The third month of the year is

   _____

4. The month staring with "S" is

   _____

5. The month before June is

   _____

Match the indoor sports with their names.

DARTS

BILLIARD

CHESS

PINBALL

Write the correct time

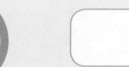

:

:

:

:

:

Match the pictures of fruit with their names.

WATERMELON

STRAWBERRY

PINEAPPLE

69

Look at the weather and write its name in the box.

Foggy
Sunny
Tornado   Snow
Cloudy
Partly Cloudy
Sleet Rain
Storm

Find 5 differences between the two pictures.

Join the dots and colour it brightly.

With the help of grid make your own Bee and colour it.

Colour the odd bubbles blue and even bubbles purple.

Count the clown fish.

Find the treasure.

Find the star fish.

Mark the insect.

19

8

10

21

33

14

24

32

48

17

85

55

63

52

88

16

18

13

22

31

27

71

How many Planets are there in the galaxy.

Find the aliens in the galaxy.

Circle those which are not found in the space.

72

Which planet gives light to the earth write its name.

Count the spaceships.

How many astronauts are there?

Circle the planet which is biggest in the space.

How many comets are there in this picture?

Find the 10 differences between two pictures.

Match the pictures with their names.

FLUTE

GUITAR

KEYBOARD

TRUMPET

DRUM

Put the fruits in their right box.

Help the elephant reach his friend zebra.

Christmas word search.

SANTA, TREE, REINDEER, WREATH, ELF, PRESENT

Match the shadows.

Match the picture to its name.

DUCK

HEN

SHEEP

GOAT

TURKEY

Solve the Earth Code.

10+7 = _____ O   14+16= _____ I

7+12= _____ T   28+9= _____ N

13+7= _____ L   19+3= _____ E

17+11= _____ U   23+6= _____ G

21+5= _____ B   6+8= _____ A

7+11= _____ R   25+6= _____ D

_____

31   17   37   19   26   22   14

_____

20   30   19   19   22   18   26   28   29

Circle the junk foods in this picture.

Count the number of balls in this picture.

Can you mark the Aliens on this beach and who is behind the surfer boat.

Find the green cola bottles.

Beach is full of surfer boats can you count them.

Find the ball with which you can't play on beach.

Find the yacht in this picture.

Count the umbrellas in this picture.

Fill in the blanks with the correct word from the box.

COW, MILK, LEGS, FARM, GRASS

1. This is a _____

2. It lives on a _____

3. It has four _____

4. It eats _____

5. It gives us _____

Match each animal with the sound it makes.

1. CHATTERS
2. TRUMPETS
3. HOOTS
4. ROARS

Circle the correct shadow.

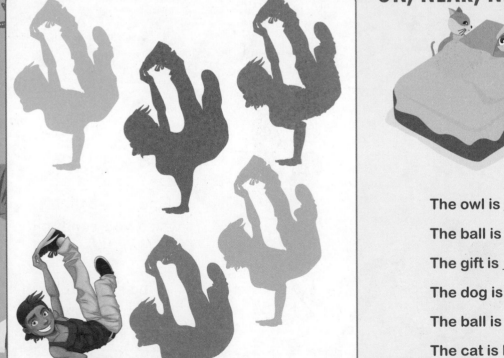

Fill in the blanks with correct preposition from the from the box.

ON, NEAR, NEXT TO, BEHIND, UNDER

The owl is _____ the bed.

The ball is _____ the table.

The gift is _____ the dog.

The dog is _____ the table.

The ball is _____ the bag.

The cat is hiding _____ the bed.

The bag is _____ the table.

Tom's dog has run away. Help him to solve maze to get his dog.

Circle the pictures that are same.

Rearrange the letters to form the sounds made by the animals and complete the sentences.

. I _____when

I see a stranger.   **ARKB**

. I _____

when I am hungry.   **MWE**

. I _____

when I sing.   **IRCHP**

. I _____

when I am in danger.   **ISHS**

Put a cross on the image that is single in the above group.

Count all the robots.

Look closely to all the robots and can you tell which star is not the part of these robots.

Match the playing cards with their other half.

Colour the picture.

PIRATE SHIP

TREASURE

PIRATE

SHARK

To know what you will get after colouring them colour the pictures by number code.

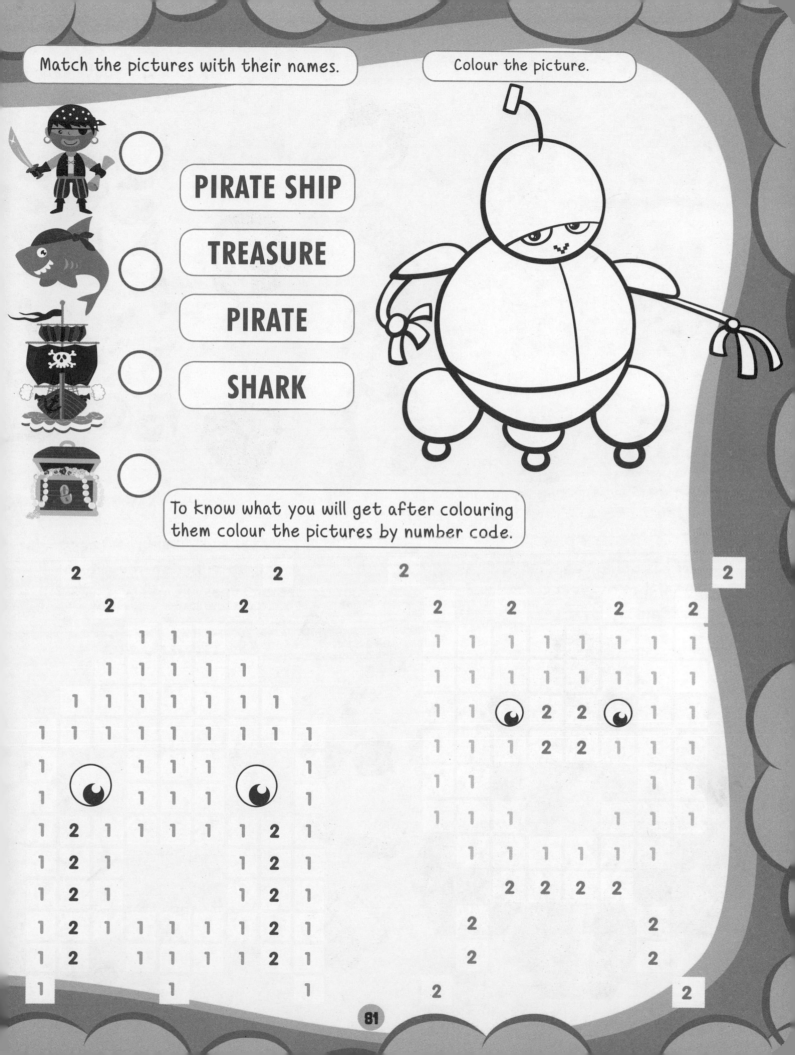

Match the hairdos with their styles.

How many footwear are there? Count them.

Merry is doing ramp walk. Can you find her correct shadow?

Girls are very found of these make-up kits. Can you match the pictures with their names?

EYE SHADOWS

LIPSTICK

GOGGLES

HAIR DRYER

Match the footwear with its matching handbag.

Colour this pretty woman with bright colours and help her go to the party.

Help the girl reach her pet.

83

Crabs are playing hide-n-seek game with kids. Can you find the hidden crabs in the sea?

Mark the girl who is holding the dolphin.

How many star fish are there? Count them.

How many sea horses can you find in this picture?

How many shells can you find in the sea?

How many fishes can you see in the whole picture? Count them.

Crazy dogs are sitting in different positions. Can you right the name of their positions?

ON, BESIDE, ABOVE, BETWEEN, IN, IN FRONT OF

Fill in the blanks with the correct word from the box.

Mark the sea creatures that can be eaten.

KENNEL, STABLE, SHED, HUTCH

Uncle Joe has a farm. There are many animals on his farm. He keeps the cows in a _____ and horses in a _____. Uncle Joe lets me take the rabbit out from the _____ and play with it. Uncle Joe has a pet dog. It sleeps in a _____ when it is not guarding the house.

85

Match each part of the fish with its name.

FIN EYE SCALE

TAIL

MOUTH BODY GILL

Find the missing piece of the picture.

1

2

3

4

Write the name of the parts of a plant shown in the picture.

Write down the new prices of these items when 15p has been taken off.

20p 25p 10p

22p 28p 30p

Find the 5 differences between two pictures.

Today we are counting lots of 5 lets go.

1. There are 5 ice-cream in each line. How many ice-cream in 5 lines

2. There are 4 cake in each line. How many cakes in 5 lines

3. There are 3 donuts in each line. How many donuts in 5 lines

4. There are 5 candy in each line. How many candies in 5 lines

Shapes have different characteristics. Let's look at the shape and fill in the blanks.

Write the numbers ten more than the numbers shown.

TRIANGLE, SQUARE, RECTANGLE

I AM A _____.

I HAVE _____ SIDES.

I HAVE _____ CORNERS.

I AM A _____.

I HAVE _____ SIDES.

I HAVE _____ CORNERS.

I AM A _____.

I HAVE _____ SIDES.

I HAVE _____ CORNERS.

53 [ ]   49 [ ]

62 [ ]   45 [ ]

28 [ ]   33 [ ]

19 [ ]   40 [ ]

10	+	25	=	35
25	-	5	=	20
43	+	8	=	51
33	+	22	=	55
55	-	25	=	30

Treasure

Map

Pirate

Shark

Island

Solve the sums and then according to the number colour code fill the colours in the butterfly.

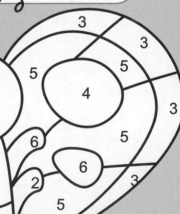

Unscramble the letters to know the name of the little fish.

2+1 =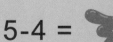

4-2 =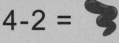

1+3 =

5-4 =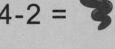

1+4 =

3+3 =

maidmer

88

Solve the problems as you travel through the maze. If your answer is an odd number, you may be going the wrong way!

Help the little butterfly reach to the flowers through the maze.

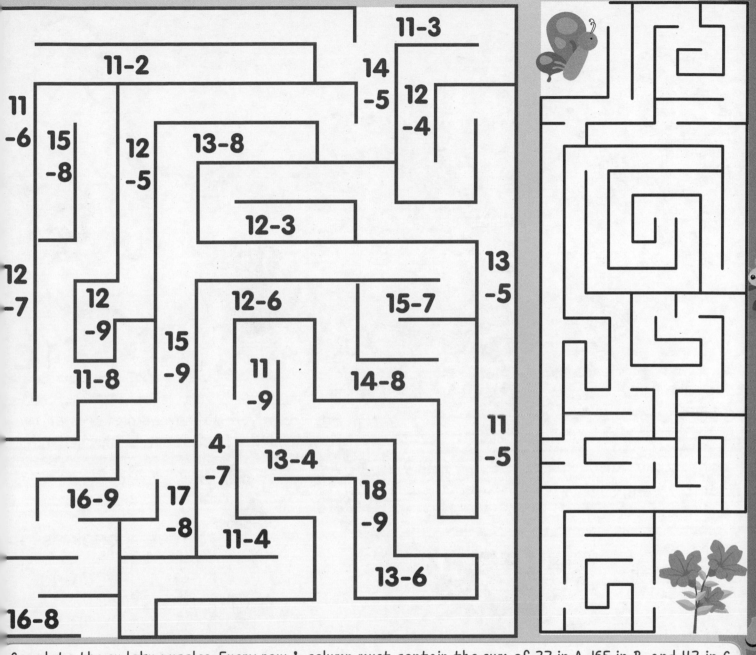

11-3
11-2
14
-5
12
-4
11
-6
15
-8
12
-5
13-8
12-3
12
-7
12
-9
12-6
15-7
13
-5
15
-9
11
-9
14-8
11-8
11
-5
16-9
17
-8
4
-7
13-4
18
-9
11-4
16-8
13-6

Complete the sudoku puzzles. Every row & column must contain the sum of 27 in A, 165 in B, and 42 in C

A

5	12	
	9	
		8

B

	55	
25	95	

C

		17
16		12
	18	

Its outing time. All are playing fishing game. Tell who is getting what in its rope.

Help Bee to get the missing part of its body from the three.

A

B

C

Can you match the pictures of my favourite food items with their names

Look at the various pieces of the funky dog. Arrange them to complete and write the serial number of the pieces.

A

B

C

D

E

toffee

cookies

pudding

donut

cupcake

ice cream

lollipop

chocolate

popsicle

cake

Circle the smallest one in each set of water animals given below.

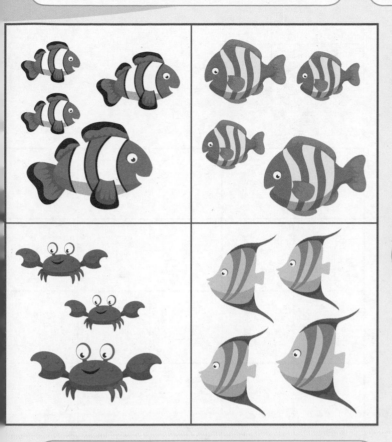

Our body is made up of many internal organs. Let's match the picture with its name.

Liver

Kidney

Lungs

Heart

Stomach

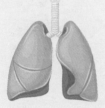

The dangerous Dinos are here! Can you match them with their shadows.

Solve the following subtraction sums and write your answer in the boxes.

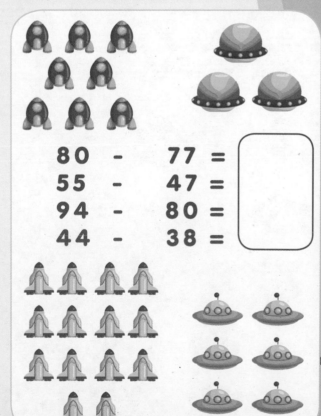

80	-	77 =	
55	-	47 =	
94	-	80 =	
44	-	38 =	

Number all of them according to their sizes. The biggest one as 1 and the smallest one is as 3.

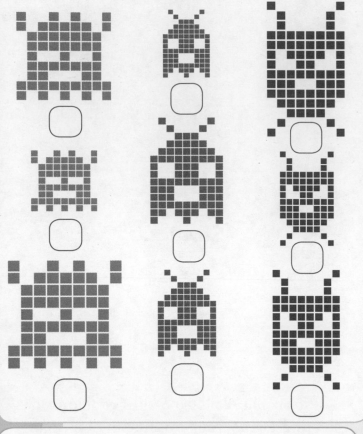

Draw the tortoise in the empty gird box and then colour it with your favourite colours.

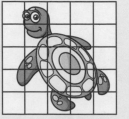

Perform some additions in accordance with the numbers assigned to the pictures.

Join all the multiple of 9 by drawing a line.

92

Hopping frog is smiling. Colour it according to the given colour code.

These all are road transport, can you help to match them with their names.

 **Bus**

 **Crane**

 **Tractor**

 **Fire brigade**

 Loader

 Double Decker

Mama Sheep lost her baby somewhere in the path. Can you help her to find the baby?

We should obey the traffic rules. Look at the pictures and match them according to their names.

 Turn Left

 No 'U' Turns

 No Parking

Two way

What the boy is looking at with the magnifying glass?

What is hanging in the girl's neck?

95

Birds are in sitting in a group.
Can you find 5 differences
between two pictures?

Insects which you see in your daily life.
Can you match their pictures with name?

A Earthworm

B Grasshopper

C Fly

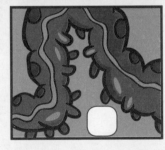

D Mosquito

Match the shadows of the elephants.

96

Find the correct path to help chick to reach his mother.

Write the correct opposite for each picture.
Good, Bad, Heavy, Light

Rockets go up in the sky. Can you count the number of rockets you see in the sky?

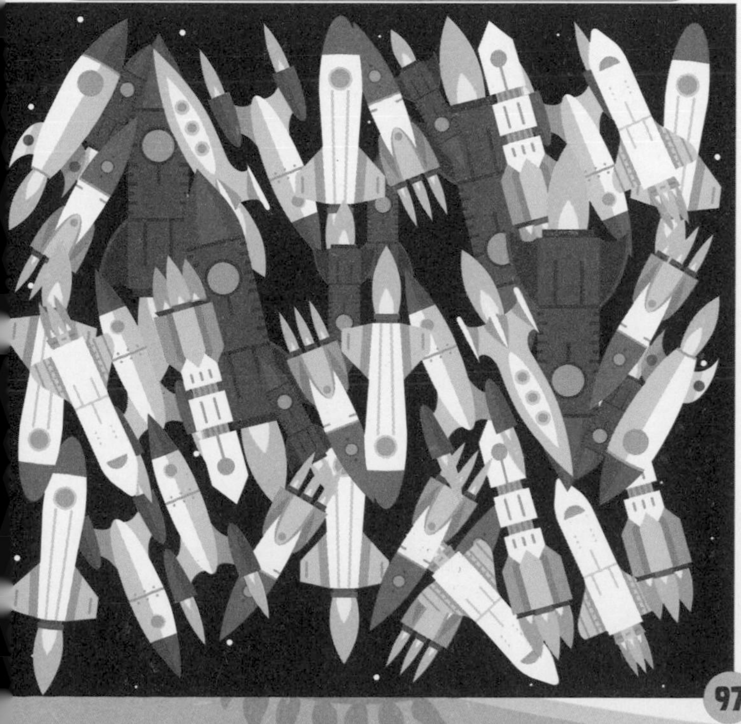

Complete the animals names.

L _ N
B _ _ R
D _ _ R
K _ _ A
R _ _ _ T
E _ _ _ _ _ T

Can you put the correct number to do addition and get the sum.

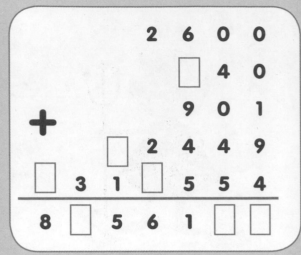

```
      2  6  0  0
         □  4  0
         9  0  1
      □  2  4  4  9
  □  3  1  □  5  5  4
+ _____
  8  □  5  6  1  □  □
```

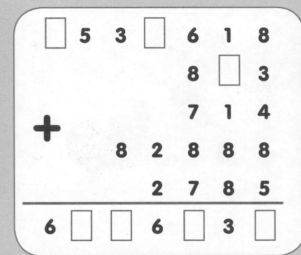

```
  □  5  3  □  6  1  8
            8  □  3
            7  1  4
         8  2  8  8  8
         2  7  8  5
+ _____
  6  □  □  6  □  3  □
```

The animal faces scared me. Can you draw a line to let me know the name of these wild animals?

These boys lost their shadows. Can you help them to match their shadow by drawing a line.

Rino	Fox	Lion	tiger	Deer

Mermaid is scared of crab, can you help her get the shell through the maze?

Colour the picture and write the name of fairytale character.

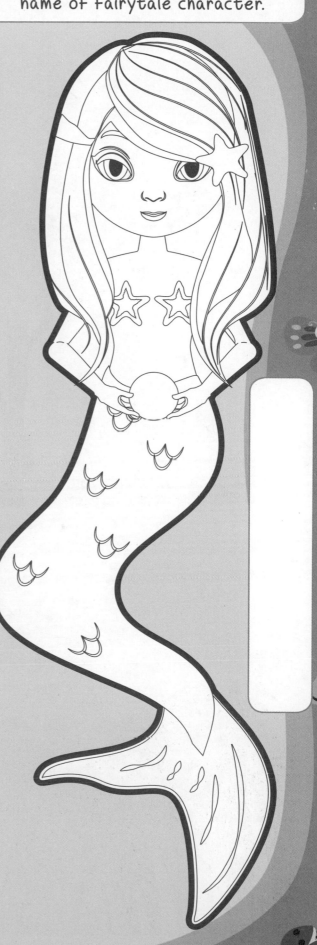

Its Halloween time! Join the dots and you will get the big vegetable, colour it.

How many apples can you see on the tree?

Birds fly in the sky. Can you mark all the birds?

How many caterpillar can you see on the green grass?

Name the crop which you can see in this farm.

How many logs can you count in this farm field?

Ants are going in a straight line. Can you count how many ants are there?

Run! Dino is here in the farm. Can you cross the Dino to save other animals?

Can you find the ladybirds in this farm field?

Do you know the names of farm animals? Write the names in given space.

Where you see the grasshoppers circle them.

Circle the beginning sound for each picture.

_ellyfish

L J I

_aguar

L I J

Add an **e** to the end of these short vowel words to make new long vowel words.

CUB — CUB_

KIT — KIT_

CAN — CAN_

PIN — PIN_

TAP — TAP_

Find all the fragments of the picture.

Solve the tricky addition sums and write the answer in given space.

18	27	84	36
+73	+86	+23	+53

Look at the picture and search the word.

Match each picture to the word that has the same rhyming sound.

G	I	D	R
B	F	O	O
E	T	G	T
A	R	E	I

LOG

BIN

SHELL

RAKE

STAR

Write the nouns in the correct groups.

BOY, LIBRARY, DOG, BALL, MOTHER, CAR, PARROT, HOSPITAL, TEACHER, SCHOOL, ELEPHANT, GLASS

See the pictures and circle their correct spellings.

PAN
PEN

DEER
DEAR

LIGHT
LITE

BREAD
BRED

KNIFE
KNEEL

CHIN
CHAIR

PEOPLE	ANIMAL

PLACE	THING

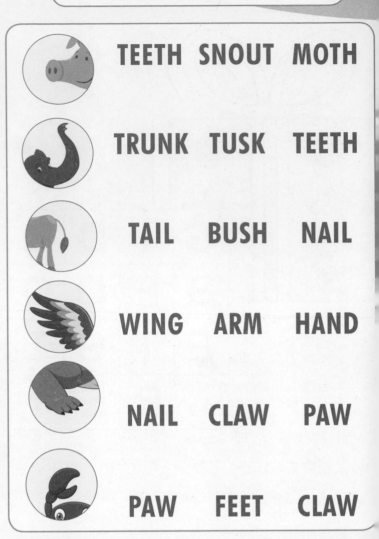

TEETH   SNOUT   MOTH

TRUNK   TUSK   TEETH

TAIL   BUSH   NAIL

WING   ARM   HAND

NAIL   CLAW   PAW

PAW   FEET   CLAW

Add the adjacent number in the pyramid and write the sum on the above block. You may use inverse operation of addition to complete the pyramid.

Alien lost his way to reach his planet, help him find his way through the maze.

4

1   3   4   5

Look at each picture and write the word in the plural form by adding '-es' at the end of the world

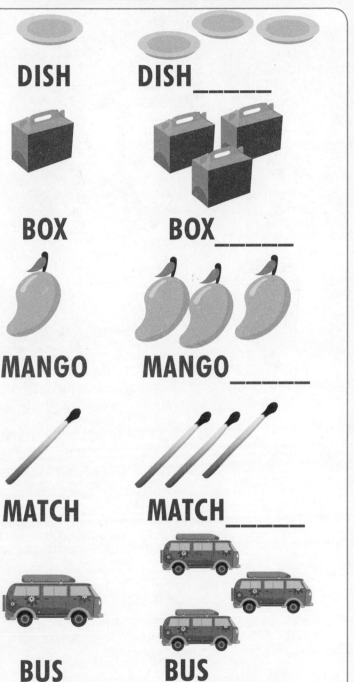

DISH   DISH_____

BOX   BOX_____

MANGO   MANGO_____

MATCH   MATCH_____

BUS   BUS_____

Have you ever tasted these food items? Can you match them with their taste?

SWEET

HOT

SALT

SOUR

BITTER

Add the adjacent number in the pyramid and write the sum on the above block. You may use inverse operation of addition to complete the pyramid.

89

54

20

4   16

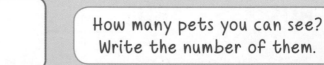

From the crowd of people, can you find out where these people are standing?

Can you count the number of people?

How many pets you can see? Write the number of them.

From the crowd of people circle who are wearing same clothes.

Look at the starred pictures and match them with the crowd and then circle the star which is not a part of this crowd.

Trace on the dotted lines and complete the picture.

Alex is doing different activities. Can you draw a line to match the picture with its name?

GOOD BYE

PLAYING DRUM

READING

PULLING

CYCLING

DRIVING

SKATING

Find the correct shadow.

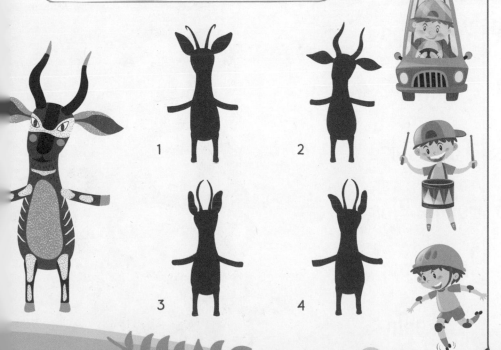

1

2

3

4

1. Those two (Man, **Men**) are brothers.

2. There are many (Child, **Children**) at the playground.

3. The (Mouse, **Mice**) are running all over the place.

4. The (Goose, **Geese**) are making a lot of noise.

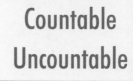
Countable
Uncountable

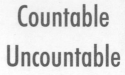
Countable
Uncountable

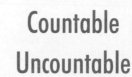
Countable
Uncountable

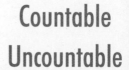
Countable
Uncountable

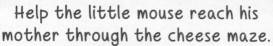
Countable
Uncountable

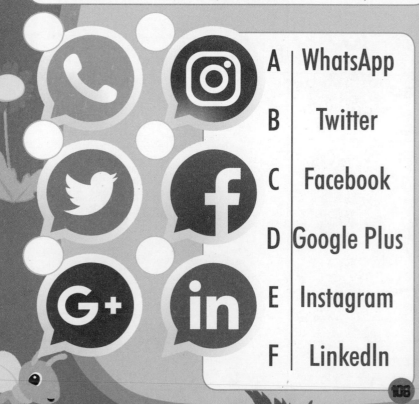

A	WhatsApp
B	Twitter
C	Facebook
D	Google Plus
E	Instagram
F	LinkedIn

Can you rearrange the letters to name the vehicle?

t e o c l r e h i p

How many Dinosaurs can you find in this picture?

Two animals do not belong to Dino family. Can you mark them?

Mark the Dinosaurs who are hiding themselves.

Find the T-rex Dino.

ount the flying Dinosaurs.

1. Mother is cutting (An, A) onion.
2. May I have (A, An) apple?
3. Eskimos live in (An, A) igloo.
4. It is raining. Take (An, A) umbrella with you.
5. (An, A) elephant has a long trunk.
6. There is (An, A) ant crawling up my leg.

Its racing time. Solve the maze and write the alphabet for the car that will come first.

A

B

C

FINISH

These are the flat pictures of animals. Can you guess their name and write in given box.

Circle the correct answer.

1 d [ ] [ ] r
2 b [ ] [ ] r
3 f [ ] [ ] h
4 f [ ] [ ] g
5 w [ ] [ ] f
6 d [ ] [ ] k
7 b [ ] [ ] d
8 l [ ] [ ] n

ir   ee   is   ol
io   ea   ro   uc

These are some pictures of trains. Can you write the correct alphabet for their names?

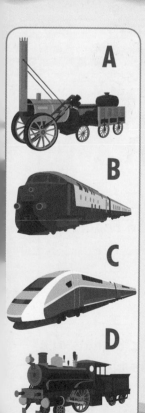

A

B

C

D

◯ **Steam rail**

◯ **Bullet train**

◯ **Diesel train**

◯ **Electric train**

I am a parrot but I don't have colours. Copy the colours and fill in me.

START

SCHOOL BUS

SCHOOL

FINISH

Help the driver to solve the road maze?

Where the bus wants to reach?

How many trees can you count?

How many Traffic Signals are there in above picture.

Mark the boards with "Men at Work".

Jungle True & False

1. Elephant cannot jump. Yes/No ○
2. Giraffe has a long neck. Yes/No ○
3. Kangaroo cannot walk backwards. Yes/No ○
4. Sharks lay the biggest eggs in the world. Yes/ No ○
5. Horses and cows sleep while standing up. Yes/No ○

Life Cycle of Butterfly. Do you know the steps of life cycle, write the alphabet against it?

Giraffe has missing one body part. Circle the correct body part to complete the giraffe.

A   B

○ EGG

○ LARGE CATERPILLAR

C

○ SMALL CATERPILLAR

D   E

○ PUPA

○ ADULT

A
B
C
D
E

We are super heroes. Find out our shadows.

This is a jungle picture. Write the correct sequence to make the jungle picture.

A B C D E

From all the witches, make the similar pair of them.

Match the correct face with their bodies. Write the correct alphabet for the same.

A

B

C

Find the fruit's name from word search.

C	O	C	O	N	U	T	X	P	M
B	P	A	P	A	Y	A	Z	O	A
K	A	V	O	C	A	D	O	M	N
I	P	N	O	R	A	N	G	E	G
W	P	F	A	G	M	A	N	G	O
I	L	S	Q	N	U	W	Y	R	S
P	E	A	R	L	A	Z	F	A	T
P	E	R	S	I	M	M	O	N	E
W	D	Q	Z	G	U	A	V	A	E
O	Z	A	P	R	I	C	O	T	N
P	I	N	E	A	P	P	L	E	R

Find the correct space shadow of space shuttle.

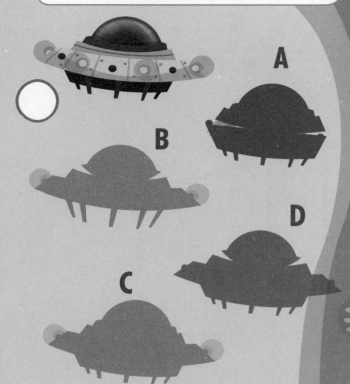

A

B

C

D

These are my dream cars. Search their names form the right side and write against them.

MICRO
CABRIOLET
MINIVAN
TRUCK
SUV
VAN
CUV
SEDAN
PICKUP
ROADSTER
SUPERCAR
COUPE
HATCHBACK
CAMPERAVAN
MINITRUCK

Fill in the blanks with correct prepositions from the box.

on   in   near   between   under

The cat is sitting _____ the chair.

The books are _____ the table.

The shoes are _____ the table.

The clock is _____ the table.

The dog is sitting _____ the box.

The table is _____ the chair and the box.

The chair is _____ the table.

Write the numbers 15 less than and 20 more than for the numbers shown.

These things are related to Halloween. How many same pairs can you make from it?

Match and make compound words of Halloween.

Broom ○ Craft _____

Cob ○ Stone _____

Eye ○ Natural _____

Grave ○ Crow _____

Moon ○ Light _____

Scare ○ Ball _____

Super ○ Web _____

Witch ○ Stick _____

This is Sara's daily routine. In the given circles write the correct sequence of her routine.

A READY FOR SCHOOL

B BRUSHING

C BREAKFAST

D DRESSING

E WAKE UP IN THE MORNING

Match the animals to they way they travel.

JUMP   FLY   SLITHER   RUN   SWIM

Colour the picture by given colour code and find out which character is coming out.

Dinos have same pattern eggs. Can you match them with their eggs?

Solve the maze for all so that they can easily go to their homes.

This is fairy tale character. Can you write her name in box.

Fill in the blanks with correct prepositions from the box.

on   in   near   behind   over

The dog is _____ the dog house.

The bird is _____ the roof.

The butterflies flying _____ the pond.

The duck swimming _____ the pond.

The fish that live _____ the pond.

The frog is hiding _____ the stone.

The duck is _____ the fish.

These are sea animals. Mark those animals which you find on the land also.

These are animal's stamps. Can you write their name against it?

This picture contains two opposite words. Write the words in the given space.

ORGANIC   GLASS   PLASTIC   PAPER

A

B

C

D

Fill in each blank with 'A' or 'An'.

Fill in each blank with 'He' 'She' or 'It'.

_____ **box**

_____ **orange**

_____ **egg**

_____ **pencil**

_____ **umbrella**

_____ **cake**

_____ **bus**

1 Mr Tan makes thnigs out of wood. _____ is a carpenter.

2 Mrs Lee teaches me in school. _____ is a teacher.

3 The cat caught a rat. _____ is eating the rat.

Its winter season. Mark the correct cap for Jasmine.

Fill in the missing letters.

P _ T A _ _

_ _ P S _ C U _

_ O _ A _ _ _

_ _ G _ L _ _ _ _

_ A _ B _ _ E _

E _ _ H _ L _ _

Fill in the blanks with is, am or are

Lets see how much you know about your body parts.

1. I have [ ] Eyes

2. I have [ ] Mouth

3. I have [ ] Ears

4. I have [ ] Fingers

5. I have [ ] Legs

6. I have [ ] Arms

7. I have [ ] Toes

1. Jack _____ swimming in the pool.
2. The school bell _____ ringing
3. I _____ Jany.
4. Ship _____ sailing in the sea.
5. I _____ not a rabbit.
6. Birds _____ flying in the sky.

Fill in the blank with the correct option.

| TOILET ROLL | BUD | TOOTH PASTE |

We clean our ears with _____

HAIR BRUSH TOOTH BRUSH TOOTH PASTE

We keep our hair neat and tidy with

_____

Can you find the 10 differences between two pictures?

Solve the maze for the witch to get shortest way to reach her house.

Can you name these hoofed animals?

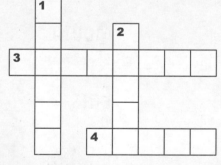

How many children are playing in the ground?

Which animal is hiding behind the bushes? Write his name.

Find and count the numbers of butterfly.

Can you see any food item in the ground? Write its name.

Write the name of the game which boys are playing.

Find 15 objects in the picture.

D	R		P
R		P	
	D		
P		N	S

E I E I A O E

Fill in the blanks of each crossword puzzle to make the multiplication equations true.

2	X		=	6

			X	

	X	1	=	

			=	

	X	24	=	

	X	5	=	30

X				

8	X	4	=	

=				

Rearrange the alphabet to get a new word.

V R E N A G E S

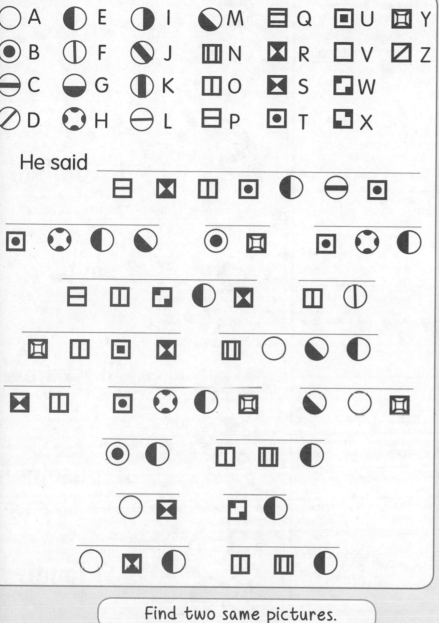

He said _____

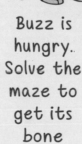

Buzz is
hungry.
Solve the
maze to
get its
bone

Find two same pictures.

Boy _____

Black _____

Young _____

Big _____

Early _____

Loud _____

Down _____

Large _____

Fast _____

Low _____

Dark _____

Hard _____

Out _____

Dry _____

Good _____

1. Football

2. Volleyball

3. Basketball

4. Baseball

5. Tennis

6. Golf

Rearrange the alphabet to get a new word.

O F D F A T O S